Revision Exercise 1

1. A particle travels at a uniform velocity, v m/s, from O to A in 4 seconds. It stops at A for 2 seconds and then returns to O at a uniform velocity of 5 m/s. The distance from O to A is 34 m.
   (a) Sketch the displacement–time graph.

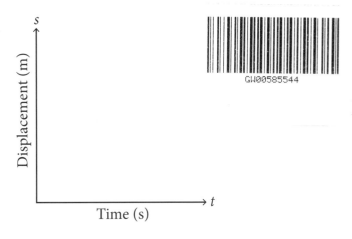

[2]

   (b) Find the value of v.

Answer _____ [1]

   (c) Find how long it takes for the whole journey.

Answer _____ s [1]

2. A particle accelerates uniformly at 1.5 m/s² for 8 seconds in travelling 64 m.
   Work out:
   (a) its initial velocity,

Answer _____ m/s [2]

   (b) its final velocity.

Answer _____ m/s [2]

3. A particle is initially at point P with position vector $(2\mathbf{i} - \mathbf{j})$ m. Its velocity at P is $(5\mathbf{i} + 2\mathbf{j})$ m/s.
   It moves with uniform acceleration $(2\mathbf{i} - 3\mathbf{j})$ m/s^2.
   Find:
   (a) its velocity after 4 seconds,

   Answer _____ m/s [2]

   (b) its position vector after 4 seconds.

   Answer _____ [3]

4. A particle rests in equilibrium at O on a smooth horizontal plane.
   It is acted upon by 4 horizontal forces of magnitude 24 N, 15 N, 12 N and P N as shown.

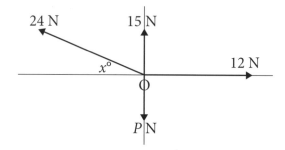

   (a) Find the value of x.

   Answer _____ [2]

   (b) Find the value of P.

   Answer _____ [2]

Neill Hamilton

CCEA GCSE

FURTHER MATHS REVISION BOOKLET
MECHANICS

COLOURPOINT
EDUCATIONAL

Contents

5. Two bodies A and B of masses 8 kg and m kg, where $m < 8$, are connected by a light inextensible string which passes over a smooth pulley as shown.

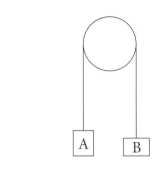

Platform

Both parts of the string are taut and hanging vertically. The system is released from rest. Each body accelerates at 1.4 m/s^2.

(a) On the diagram mark all the forces acting on the bodies. [1]

Find:

(b) the tension in the string,

Answer _____N [1]

(c) the value of m,

Answer _____kg [1]

(d) the force exerted by the string on the pulley once the bodies are in motion.

Answer _____N [1]

When the boxes have been in motion for 2.3 seconds, A strikes a fixed platform. The string becomes slack and B initially continues to rise.

Assuming B does not reach the pulley, calculate:

(e) the speed of the boxes when A strikes the platform,

Answer _____m/s [2]

(f) the **additional** distance through which B rises after A strikes the platform,

Answer _____m [2]

(g) the time which elapses between A striking the platform and the string becoming taut again.

Answer _____s [2]

6. A girl stands 5.6 m above horizontal ground. She throws a ball vertically upwards with a speed of 4.8 m/s. Find:

(a) its greatest height above the **ground**,

Answer _____m [3]

(b) the speed of the ball as it hits the ground,

Answer _____m/s [2]

(c) the time between the ball being thrown and hitting the ground.

Answer _____s [3]

7. A uniform plank AB of mass 36 kg and length 10 m rests horizontally on two supports at C and D where AC = 2.2 m and DB = 3 m.

A child of mass 28 kg stands at the centre of the plank.
(a) On the diagram mark all the forces acting on the plank.   [2]
(b) Find the reactions at C and D.

Answer _____N [3]

The child now moves towards B until the plank is on the point of tilting about D.
(c) State the value of the reaction at C.

Answer _____N [1]

(d) Calculate the distance from the child to B.

Answer _____m [2]

8. A box of mass 5 kg is held at rest on the surface of a rough plane which is inclined at 27° to the horizontal.

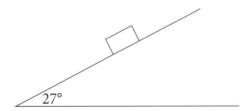

It is released from rest and accelerates uniformly down the plane at an acceleration of 1.4 m/s².
(a) On the diagram mark all the forces acting on the box.   [1]

Calculate:

(b) the normal reaction of the plane on the box,

Answer _____N [1]

(c) the magnitude of the frictional force acting on the box,

Answer _____N [1]

(d) the time it takes the box to reach a speed of 2.1 m/s.

Answer _____s [2]

Once the box reaches 2.1 m/s it is stopped.
(e) Calculate the force parallel to the plane needed to hold the box in equilibrium on the plane.

Answer _____N [2]

Revision Exercise 2

1. A particle accelerates uniformly from 3 m/s to 8 m/s in 4 seconds.
   It then continues at 8 m/s for 3 seconds.
   It then decelerates uniformly to rest in a further 5 seconds.
   (a) Sketch the velocity–time graph.

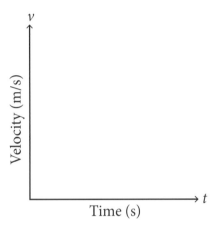

[2]

   (b) Find the acceleration in the first part of the motion.

Answer _____ m/s² [2]

   (c) Find the deceleration in the last part of the motion.

Answer _____ m/s² [1]

   (d) Work out the total distance travelled.

Answer _____ m [3]

2. A particle accelerates uniformly from 6 m/s to 18 m/s in travelling 48 m.
   Work out:
   (a) its acceleration,

   Answer _____m/s^2 [2]

   (b) the time taken.

   Answer _____s [2]

3. A body of mass 5 kg is initially at rest at O. It is acted upon by two forces, $\mathbf{P} = (7\mathbf{i} - 2\mathbf{j})$ N and $\mathbf{Q} = (-3\mathbf{i} - \mathbf{j})$ N.
   (a) Find the resultant of the two forces $\mathbf{P}$ and $\mathbf{Q}$.

   Answer _____ [2]

   The body moves with acceleration $(x\mathbf{i} + y\mathbf{j})$ m/s^2.
   (b) Find the values of x and y.

   Answer _____ [2]

   It reaches point P after 3 seconds.
   (c) Find the displacement vector $\mathbf{OP}$.

   Answer _____ [2]

4. A box of mass M kg is suspended from O by a light inextensible string.
It is pulled aside by a force of 36 N which acts at 52° with the horizontal as shown.

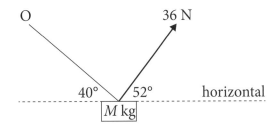

The box hangs in equilibrium with the string making 40° with the horizontal.
Find:
(a) the tension T newtons in the string,

Answer _____N [2]

(b) the mass m kg of the box.

Answer _____kg [2]

5. Two bodies A and B of masses 6 kg and m kg, where $m < 6$, are connected by a light inextensible string which passes over a smooth pulley.

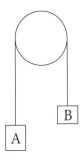

Both parts of the string are taut and hanging vertically. The system is released from rest. The tension in the string is 51 N.
Calculate:
(a) the acceleration of each body,

Answer _____m/s^2 [2]

(b) the value of *m*.

Answer _____ kg [2]

6. A block of mass 4.7 kg is initially at rest on a smooth horizontal table.
   It is pulled along the table by a string with force *F* N.
   The string makes an angle of 38° with the horizontal.
   The block accelerates at 2.25 m/s².

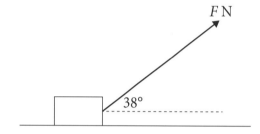

(a) On the diagram mark all the other forces acting on the block. [2]

Calculate:

(b) the value of *F*.

Answer _____ N [2]

(c) the value of the normal reaction between the block and the table.

Answer _____ N [2]

(d) the time it takes the block to move 6 m.

Answer _____ s [2]

7. A seesaw is made of a uniform wooden plank AB of mass 16 kg and length 8 m.
   Willow, of mass M kg, sits at A. Rory of mass 31 kg sits at B.
   The seesaw is supported horizontally by a smooth pivot at P, remaining in equilibrium as shown.
   PB = 3.8 m.

A ———————————————————— P ———————————— B

(a) On the diagram mark all the forces acting on the seesaw.   [2]

Calculate:
(b) the value of the reaction at P.

                                                                    Answer _____N [3]

(c) the value of M.

                                                                    Answer _____kg [2]

8. A box of mass 18 kg accelerates down a rough plane which is inclined at $\theta°$ to the horizontal

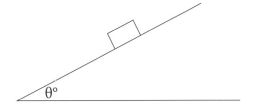

θ°

   It accelerates uniformly from a speed of 1.8 m/s for 2 s travelling 5.1 m down the plane.
   The magnitude of the frictional force is 48 N.
   (a) On the diagram mark all the forces acting on the box.   [1]

Calculate:
(b) the value of θ,

                                                                    Answer _____° [4]

(c) the normal reaction of the plane on the box.

Answer _____N [2]

The box is then held in equilibrium on this plane by a force F N parallel to the plane.

(d) Calculate the value of F.

Answer _____N [2]

Total for revision exercise [50]

Revision Exercise 3

1. A car travels at a uniform velocity of 15 m/s for T seconds.
   It then accelerates uniformly at 0.96 m/s^2 for 4 seconds until it reaches its maximum velocity.
   It then decelerates uniformly to rest in a further 10 seconds.
   (a) Calculate the maximum velocity.

   Answer _____ m/s [2]

   (b) Sketch the velocity–time graph for the journey.

   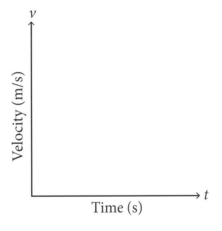

   [2]

   (c) Calculate the deceleration.

   Answer _____ m/s^2 [2]

   (d) Given that the total distance travelled is 221.88 m calculate the value of T.

   Answer _____ s [3]

2. A particle decelerates uniformly, reaching a velocity of 3 m/s in 2.5 s covering 13.75 m.
   Work out:
   (a) its initial velocity,

   Answer _____ m/s [2]

   (b) its deceleration.

   Answer _____ m/s² [2]

3. A body of mass 4 kg is initially at rest at O. It is acted upon by a force **F** which makes it accelerate at
   $(6\mathbf{i} + 10\mathbf{j})$ m/s².
   (a) Find the force **F**.

   Answer _____ N [1]

   After 1½ seconds the body is at point P.
   (b) Find the vector **OP**.

   Answer _____ [2]

   (c) Find its speed after 5 seconds.

   Answer _____ m/s [3]

4. A body of mass 6 kg is held in equilibrium at a point C by 2 light chains CA and CB.
The chains are inclined at 20° and 45° to the horizontal as shown.

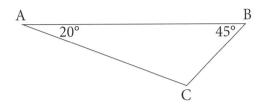

(a) Mark on all the forces acting on the body at C. [2]

(b) Calculate the tensions in the chains CA and CB.

Answer _____N [4]

5. A car of mass 910 kg tows a trailer of mass *M* kg along a straight horizontal road.
The car and trailer are connected by a light inextensible towbar as shown.

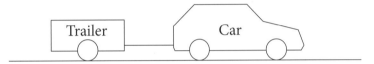

The resistance to motion of the car is 1.14 N per kg.
The resistance to motion of the trailer is 0.87 N per kg.
The tractive force of the engine of the car is 2.5 kN.
The tension in the towbar is 652 N.
Calculate:

(a) the acceleration of the car and trailer,

Answer _____m/s^2 [2]

(b) the value of *M*.

Answer _____kg [1]

The car and trailer start from rest.
Six seconds later the towbar breaks.

(c) Calculate the speed of the car when the towbar breaks.

Answer _____m/s [1]

(d) Calculate the speed of the car 10 seconds after the towbar breaks.

Answer _____m/s [2]

6. A marble is thrown vertically upwards from 1.8 m above ground level at a velocity of 5.4 m/s.
   Find:
   (a) the time it takes to reach its greatest height,

Answer _____s [2]

(b) the greatest height above ground level reached by the marble,

Answer _____m [2]

(c) the times between which the marble is 2.9 m above ground level.

Answer _____s and _____s [3]

7. A uniform plank AB of mass 0.96 kg rests horizontally in equilibrium on two supports at A and C where CB = 1.2 m as shown.

The reaction at C is double the reaction at A.
(a) On the diagram mark all the forces acting on the plank.   [1]

Calculate:
(b) the value of the reactions at A and C,

Answer _____N [2]

(c) the length of the plank.

Answer _____m [3]

8. A box of mass 5.6 kg rests on the surface of a rough plane which is inclined at 30° to the horizontal.

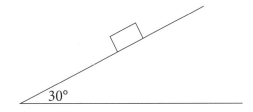

The box is just on the point of sliding down the plane.
(a) On the diagram mark all the forces acting on the box.   [2]

Calculate:
(b) the magnitude of the frictional force,

Answer _____N [1]

(c) the normal reaction of the plane on the box.

Answer _____N [1]

The box is now pulled up the plane with a constant velocity by a light inextensible string parallel to the plane. The string exerts a force of P N on the box.

(d) Calculate the value of P.

Answer _____N [2]

Total for revision exercise [**50**]

Revision Exercise 4

1. Sean leaves a point P walking at a uniform velocity of 1.5 m/s.
   Aideen leaves P 8 seconds later. She rides a bike from rest at a uniform acceleration of 0.4 m/s² for 7 seconds
   until she reaches a maximum velocity. She continues at this velocity until she overtakes Sean.
   (a) Draw a velocity–time graph to show both journeys.

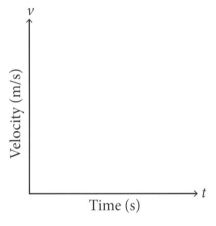

                                                                                                              [2]
   (b) Calculate the time Sean has been walking when Aideen overtakes him.

                                                          Answer _____s [4]

   (c) Calculate the distance from P when Aideen overtakes Sean.

                                                          Answer _____m [1]

2. A particle accelerates uniformly at 3 m/s². It increases its velocity from 2 m/s to 14 m/s.
   Work out:
   (a) the time taken,

                                                          Answer _____s [2]

(b) its displacement from the start.

Answer _____m [2]

3. A body of mass 15 kg, initially at O, accelerates uniformly from a velocity of $(2\mathbf{i} - 3\mathbf{j})$ m/s to a velocity of $(4\mathbf{i} - 13\mathbf{j})$ m/s in 5 seconds.
   (a) Find the displacement from O after 5 seconds.

Answer _____m [2]

A force **F** is then applied to the body causing it to come to rest in a further 10 seconds.
(b) Find the acceleration of the body.

Answer _____m/s² [2]

(c) Find the value of **F**.

Answer _____N [1]

(d) Find the magnitude of **F**.

Answer _____N [1]

4. A body of mass 16 kg is resting on a smooth horizontal surface AB.
   It is acted upon by a horizontal force of 144 N and by a force of 170 N inclined at θ° to the horizontal.

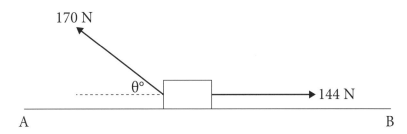

The body remains in equilibrium.
Find:
(a) the value of θ,

Answer _____° [2]

(b) the normal reaction between the surface and the body.

Answer _____N [2]

5. A car of mass M kg tows a trailer of mass 480 kg by means of a light horizontal towbar as shown. The tractive force of the car's engine is 3.91 kN.

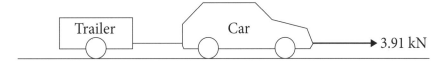

The car and trailer accelerate uniformly from rest to 18 m/s in driving 108 m.
The total resistance to the motion is 1456 N.
Calculate:
(a) the acceleration,

Answer _____m/s² [1]

(b) the value of M.

Answer _____kg [2]

The resistance to the motion of the car is 0.684 N per kg of mass.
Calculate:

(c) the resistance to the motion of the car,

Answer _____N [1]

(d) the resistance to the motion of the trailer,

Answer _____N [1]

(e) the magnitude of the tension in the towbar.

Answer _____N [2]

The car and trailer then travel at a constant speed of 18 m/s and after a while the towbar breaks.

(f) Calculate the time it takes the trailer to come to rest, assuming the resistance to its motion stays the same.

Answer _____s [2]

6. A box of mass 12.5 kg is placed on a **smooth** plane inclined at $\theta°$ to the horizontal.
    It is prevented from sliding down the plane by a force of 86 N as shown.

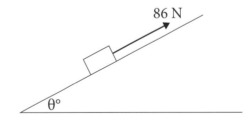

(a) On the diagram mark all the forces acting on the box.   [2]

(b) Calculate the value of θ.

Answer _____° [1]

(c) Calculate the normal reaction between the box and the plane.

Answer _____N [1]

The force of 86 N is now replaced by a force of Q N acting along the line of greatest slope causing the box to move 1.5 m to the top of the plane in 7s.
(d) Calculate the value of Q.

Answer _____N [3]

7. A uniform rod AB of length 6m and mass 3.2 kg rests horizontally in equilibrium on two supports at C and D where AC = 0.8m as shown. A mass is placed at A and another mass, three times as heavy, is placed at B.

A ——— C ————————————————— D ——— B
   0.8 m △   △

The reaction at C is 16 N and the reaction at D is 88 N.
(a) On the diagram mark all the forces acting on the rod.   [2]

Calculate:
(b) the value of the masses at A and B,

Answer A = _____kg and B = _____kg [2]

(c) the length of DB.

Answer _____m [2]

The supports at C and D are removed and replaced by a single support at E, which is *d* metres from A as shown below.

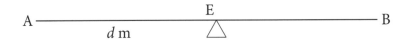

The rod remains horizontal and in equilibrium.

(d) Calculate the value of *d*.

Answer _____ m [2]

8. A box of mass 4 kg is initially at rest on a rough plane which is inclined at 20° to the horizontal. It is pulled up the plane by a force of 35 N acting parallel to the plane.

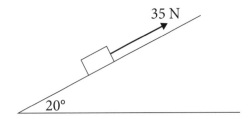

The box is just on the point of sliding down the plane.

(a) On the diagram mark all the forces acting on the box. [1]

It accelerates uniformly from 3 m/s to 8 m/s in a distance of 10 m.

(b) Calculate the magnitude of the frictional force.

Answer _____ N [2]

The 35 N force is then removed.

(c) Calculate the additional time the box will move.

Answer _____ s [2]

Total for revision exercise [**50**]

Revision Exercise 5

1. A lorry travels at a uniform velocity of 16 m/s.
   A car, at rest, is at a point P.
   When the lorry passes P the car instantaneously accelerates uniformly for 35 seconds until it reaches a velocity of 24 m/s.
   It then continues at this velocity until it overtakes the lorry.
   (a) Draw a velocity–time graph to show both journeys.

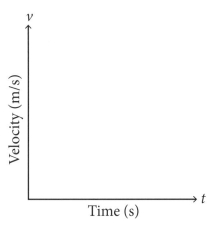

[2]

   (b) How long altogether has the car been moving when it overtakes the lorry?

                                                    Answer _____ s [4]

   (c) Calculate the distance which the car has travelled in overtaking the lorry.

                                                    Answer _____ m [1]

2. A body moving at 6 m/s comes to rest uniformly in 8 seconds.
   Work out:
   (a) the deceleration,

                                                    Answer _____ m/s² [2]

(b) the distance covered.

Answer _____m [2]

3. A body mass 4 kg is acted upon by 3 forces **P** = (*x***i** + 3**j**) N, **Q** = (5**i** – 2*y***j**) N and **R** =(–7**i** + 10**j**) N.
   (a) The body is in equilibrium Find the values of *x* and *y*.

Answer *x* = _____ *y* = _____ [2]

The forces **P** and **Q** are now removed.
(b) Find the acceleration of the body.

Answer _____m/s² [2]

(c) Find the acute angle the acceleration makes with the positive *x*-axis.

Answer _____° [2]

4. Three forces act at a point A as shown:
   A force *W* N is vertical.
   A force of 48 N is horizontal.
   A force of *V* N acts at 34° to the horizontal.

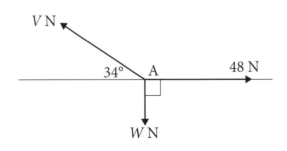

The resultant is a single force of 24 N acting at 64° to the horizontal as shown.

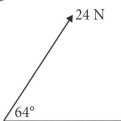

Calculate:
(a) the value of *V*.

Answer _____N [2]

(b) the value of *W*.

Answer _____N [2]

5. Two bodies of mass 2.4 kg and 5.6 kg are connected by a light inextensible string which passes over a smooth pulley. The 2.4 kg lies on a smooth horizontal table and the 5.6 kg hangs freely as shown.

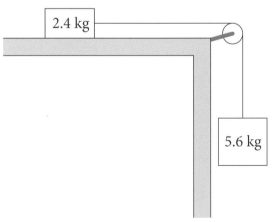

The system is released from rest.
(a) On the diagram mark all the forces acting on the two bodies.   [2]

Calculate:
(b) the acceleration of the system,

Answer _____m/s² [2]

(c) the tension in the string,

Answer _____N [1]

(d) the time it takes the 5.6 kg body to fall 70 cm, assuming the 2.4 kg mass does not reach the pulley.

Answer _____N [2]

6. A body of mass 13.5 kg is placed on a smooth plane AB.
It is acted upon by a force of 146 N at θ° to the horizontal and by a force of 120 N as shown.

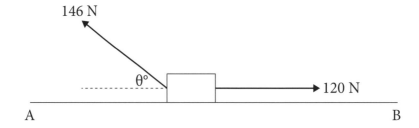

The body remains in equilibrium.
Calculate:
(a) the value of θ,

Answer _____° [2]

(b) the normal reaction between the body and the plane.

Answer _____N [2]

The force of 146 N is now replaced by a horizontal force of Q N acting to the left causing the body to accelerate at 1.2 m/s² towards B.

(c) Calculate the value of Q.

Answer _____ N [2]

7. A uniform beam AB of length 11 m and mass 16.5 kg is suspended from a ceiling by two vertical cables attached at C and D.

AC = 1.8 m.

The tension in the cable at D is double the tension in the cable at C.

The beam hangs in equilibrium horizontally.

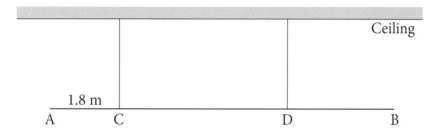

(a) On the diagram mark all the forces acting on the rod.   [1]

Calculate:

(b) the tension in each cable,

Answer _____ N [2]

(c) the length of DB,

Answer _____ m [2]

(d) how far from B a mass of 23 kg should be placed to equalise the tensions in the cables.

Answer _____ m [3]

8. A block of mass 42 kg is lying on a rough horizontal plane.
   A rope inclined at 56° to the horizontal pulls it along the plane at a constant velocity of 2.5 m/s.
   The magnitude of the frictional force is 126 N.

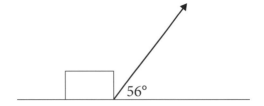

(a) On the diagram mark all the forces acting on the block. [2]

(b) Calculate the tension T in the rope.

Answer _____N [2]

(c) Calculate the normal reaction between the block and the plane.

Answer _____N [2]

(d) Assuming the tension in the rope and the frictional force remain the same, calculate how much the angle of 56° needs to be reduced by to make the block accelerate at 0.36 m/s².

Answer _____° [2]

Answers

Revision Exercise 1

1. (a)

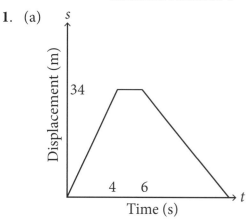

[2]

(b) $v = 34 \div 4 = 8.5$ m/s [1]

(c) $34 \div 5 = 6.8$; $6.8 + 4 + 2 = 12.8$ s [1]

2. (a) $s = ut + \frac{1}{2}at^2$, $64 = 8u + 48$, $u = 2$ m/s [M1W1]

(b) $v = u + at = 2 + 12 = 14$ m/s [M1W1]

3. (a) $v = u + at = (5\mathbf{i} + 2\mathbf{j}) + 4(2\mathbf{i} - 3\mathbf{j})$
$= (13\mathbf{i} - 10\mathbf{j})$ m/s [M1W1]

(b) $s = \frac{1}{2}t(u + v) = 2(18\mathbf{i} - 8\mathbf{j}) = 36\mathbf{i} - 16\mathbf{j}$
Answer: $2\mathbf{i} - \mathbf{j} + 36\mathbf{i} - 16\mathbf{j} = (38\mathbf{i} - 17\mathbf{j})$ m [M1W2]

4. (a) Resolve horizontally.
$24 \cos x = 12$; $\cos x = 0.5$; $x = 60°$ [M1W1]

(b) Resolve vertically. $P = 24 \sin 60 + 15 = 35.78$ [M1W1]

5. (a)

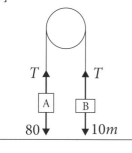

[1]

(b) Body A: $F = ma$; $80 - T = 8 \times 1.4$;
$T = 68.8$ N [1]

(c) Body B: $F = ma$; $68.8 - 10m = m \times 1.4$;
$m = 6.04$ kg [1] (d) $68.8 \times 2 = 137.6$ N [1]

(e) $v = u + at = 0 + 1.4 \times 2.3 = 3.22$ m/s [M1W1]

(f) $u = 3.22$, $v = 0$, $a = -10$
$v^2 = u^2 + 2as$; $0 = 10.3684 - 20s$; $s = 0.51842$ m [M1W1]

(g) $v = u + at$; $0 = 3.22 - 10t$; $t = 0.322$ s
Time until taut $= 0.322 \times 2 = 0.644$ s [M1W1]

6. (a) $u = 4.8$; $v = 0$; $a = -10$
$v^2 = u^2 + 2as$; $0 = 23.04 - 20s$; $s = 1.152$

Greatest height $= 1.152 + 5.6 = 6.752$ m [M1W2]

(b) $u = 0$; $a = 10$; $s = 6.752$
$v^2 = u^2 + 2as = 2 \times 10 \times 6.752 = 135.04$;
$v = 11.62$ m/s [M1W1]

(c) Up: $u = 4.8$; $v = 0$; $a = -10$; $v = u + at$;
$0 = 4.8 - 10t$; $t = 0.48$
Down: $u = 0$; $a = 10$; $s = 6.752$
$s = ut + \frac{1}{2}at^2$; $6.752 = 5t^2$; $t = 1.162$
Total time $= 1.162 + 0.48 = 1.64$ s [3]

7. (a)

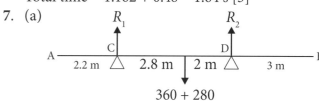

[M1W1]

(b) Moments at C:
$R_2 \times 4.8 = 640 \times 2.8$; $R_2 = 373.33$ N
$R_1 + R_2 = 640$; giving $R_1 = 266.67$ N [M1W2]

(c) Reaction at C $= 0$ N [1]

(d)

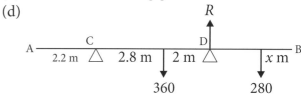

Moments at D: $360 \times 2 = 280(3 - x)$;
$x = 0.43$ m [M1W1]

8. (a)

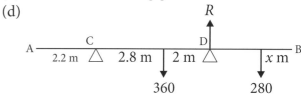

[1]

(b) $R = 50 \cos 27 = 44.55$ N [1]

(c) $F = ma$; $50 \sin 27 - F = 5 \times 1.4$; $F = 15.70$ N [1]

(d) $u = 0$, $a = 1.4$, $v = 2.1$
$v = u + at$; $2.1 = 1.4t$, so $t = 1.5$ s [M1W1]

(e) Force $+ 15.70 = 50 \sin 27$; giving Force $= 7$ N [M1W1]

Revision Exercise 2

1. (a)

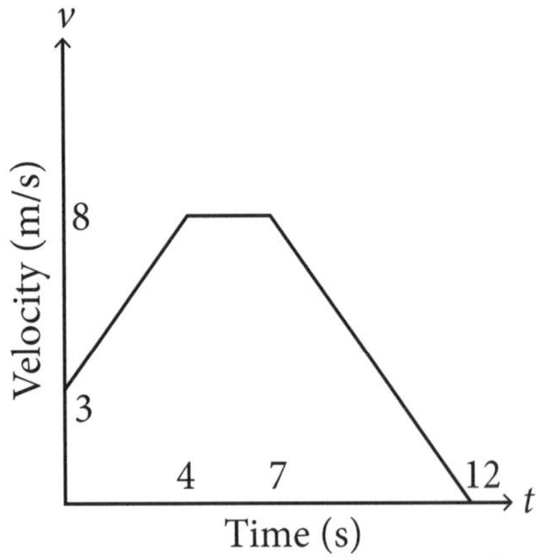

[2]

(b) $a = 5 \div 4 = 1.25$ m/s^2 [M1W1]

(c) $8 \div 5 = 1.6$ m/s^2 [1]

(d) $\frac{1}{2}(3 + 8) \times 4 + 3 \times 8 + \frac{1}{2} \times 5 \times 8$
$= 22 + 24 + 20 = 66$ m [M2W1]

2. (a) $v^2 = u^2 + 2as$; $324 = 36 + 96a$; $a = 3$ m/s^2 [M1W1]

(b) $v = u + at$; $18 = 6 + 3t$; $t = 4$ s [M1W1]

3. (a) $(7\mathbf{i} - 2\mathbf{j}) + (-3\mathbf{i} - \mathbf{j}) = (4\mathbf{i} - 3\mathbf{j})$ N [M1W1]

(b) $F = ma$; $(4\mathbf{i} - 3\mathbf{j}) = 5a$; $a = (\frac{4}{5}\mathbf{i} - \frac{3}{5}\mathbf{j})$
$x = \frac{4}{5}$ and $y = -\frac{3}{5}$ [M1W1]

(c) $s = ut + \frac{1}{2}at^2 = \frac{9}{2}(\frac{4}{5}\mathbf{i} - \frac{3}{5}\mathbf{j}) = (3.6\mathbf{i} - 2.7\mathbf{j})$ m [M1W1]

4. (a) Resolve horizontally: $T \cos 40 = 36 \cos 52$;
$T = 36 \cos 52 \div \cos 40 = 28.93$ N [M1W1]

(b) Resolve vertically: $10m = 28.933 \sin 40 + 36 \sin 52$
$= 46.966$; $m = 4.70$ kg [M1W1]

5. (a) Body A: $F = ma$; $60 - 51 = 6a$; $a = 1.5$ m/s^2 [M1W1]

(b) Body B: $51 - 10m = 1.5m$; $11.5m = 51$;
$m = 4.43$ kg [M1W1]

6. (a)

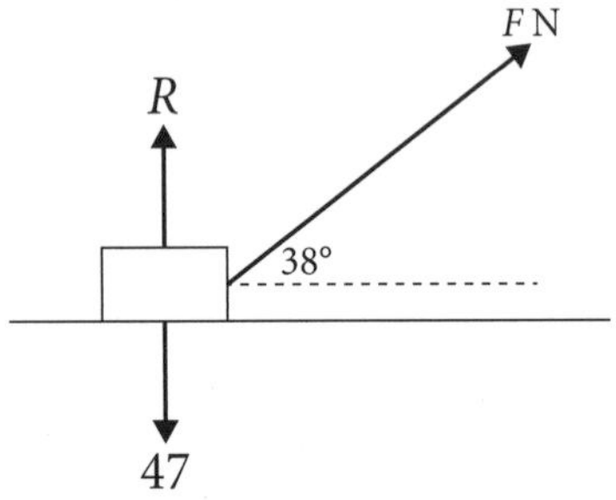

[2]

(b) Resolve horizontally: $F = ma$
$F \cos 38 = 4.7 \times 2.25 = 10.575$; $F = 13.42$ N [M1W1]

(c) Resolve vertically: $R + 13.42 \sin 38 = 47$
$R = 38.74$ N [M1W1]

(d) $u = 0$; $a = 2.25$; $s = 6$;
$s = ut + \frac{1}{2}at^2$; $6 = 1.125t^2$; $t = 2.31$ s [M1W1]

7. (a)

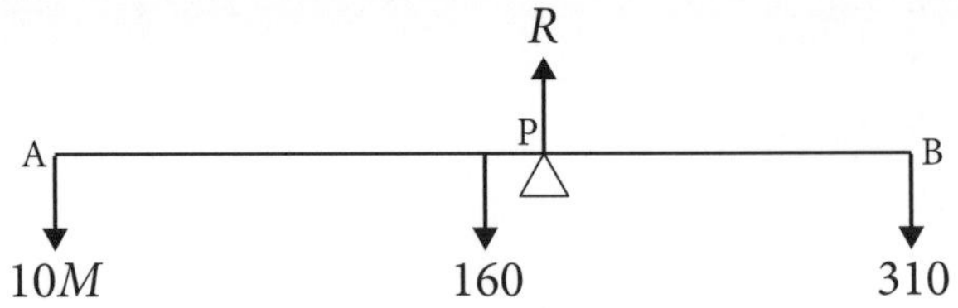

[2] ([1] for 2 or 3 correct forces)

(b) Moments at A: $R \times 4.2 = 160 \times 4 + 310 \times 8$
$R = 742.86$ N [M2W1]

(c) $10M + 160 + 310 = 742.86$; $M = 27.29$ kg [M1W1]

8. (a)

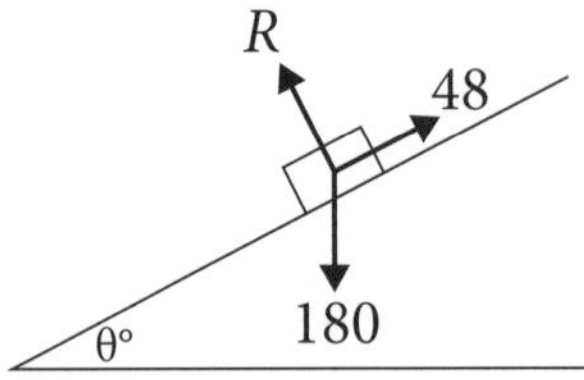

[1]

(b) $u = 1.8$; $t = 2$; $s = 5.1$; $s = ut + \frac{1}{2}at^2$; $a = 0.75$
$F = ma$; $180 \sin \theta - 48 = 18 \times 0.75$; $\theta = 19.98°$ [M2W2]

(c) $R = 180 \cos 19.98 = 169.17$ N [M1W1]

(d) Force + 48 = 180 sin 19.98, so Force = 13.50 N [M1W1]

Revision Exercise 3

1. (a) $u = 15$; $a = 0.96$; $t = 4$
$v = u + at = 15 + 0.96 \times 4 = 18.84$ m/s [M1W1]

(b)

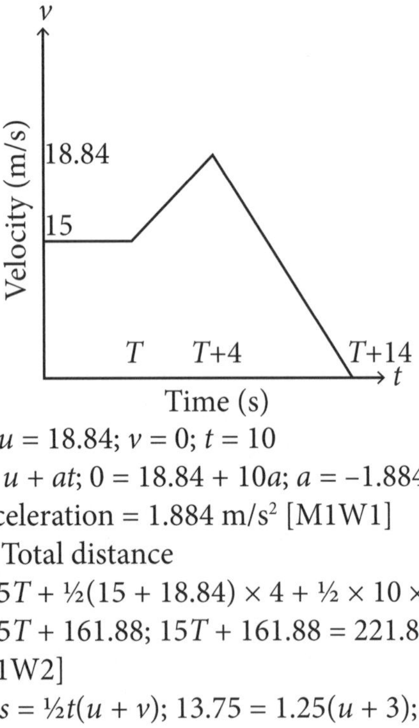

[2]

(c) $u = 18.84$; $v = 0$; $t = 10$
$v = u + at$; $0 = 18.84 + 10a$; $a = -1.884$
Deceleration = 1.884 m/s^2 [M1W1]

(d) Total distance
$= 15T + \frac{1}{2}(15 + 18.84) \times 4 + \frac{1}{2} \times 10 \times 18.84$
$= 15T + 161.88$; $15T + 161.88 = 221.88$ so $T = 4$ [M1W2]

2. (a) $s = \frac{1}{2}t(u + v)$; $13.75 = 1.25(u + 3)$; $u = 8$ m/s [M1W1]

(b) $v = u + at$; $3 = 8 + 2.5a$; $a = -2$
Deceleration = 2 m/s^2 [M1W1]

3. (a) $F = ma = 4(6\mathbf{i} + 10\mathbf{j}) = (24\mathbf{i} + 40\mathbf{j})$ N [1]

(b) $s = ut + \frac{1}{2}at^2 = \frac{9}{8}(6\mathbf{i} + 10\mathbf{j}) = (6.75\mathbf{i} + 11.25\mathbf{j})$ m [M1W1]

(c) $v = u + at = 5(6\mathbf{i} + 10\mathbf{j}) = 30\mathbf{i} + 50\mathbf{j}$
Speed $= \sqrt{30^2 + 50^2} = \sqrt{3400} = 58.31$ m/s [M1W2]

4. (a)

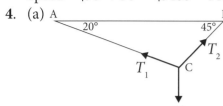

[2] ([1] for 1 correct force)

(b) Resolve horizontally: $T_1 \cos 20 - T_2 \cos 45 = 0$
Resolve vertically: $T_1 \sin 20 + T_2 \sin 45 = 60$
Adding these gives $T_1(\cos 20 + \sin 20) = 60$
so $T_1 = 46.81$ N. Substituting gives
$T_2 \cos 45 = 46.81 \cos 20$, so $T_2 = 62.21$ N [M2W2]

5.

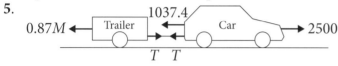

(a) Car: The resistance to motion of the car
$= 1.14 \times 910 = 1037.4$
$F = ma$; $2500 - 652 - 1037.4 = 910a$; $a = 0.89$ m/s^2
[M1W1]
(b) Trailer: The resistance to motion of the trailer
$= 0.87 \times M$
$F = ma$; $652 - 0.87M = 0.89M$; so $M = 370$ kg [1]
(c) $u = 0$; $a = 0.89$; $t = 6$
$v = u + at = 0.89 \times 6 = 5.34$ m/s [M1W1]
(d) $F = ma$; $2500 - 1037.4 = 1462.6 = 910a$
$a = 1.607$; $u = 5.34$; $t = 10$; $v = u + at = 21.41$ m/s

6. (a) $u = 5.4$; $a = -10$; $v = 0$
$v = u + at$; $0 = 5.4 - 10t$; $t = 0.54$ s [M1W1]
(b) $v^2 = u^2 + 2as$; $0 = 29.16 - 20s$; $s = 1.458$
$1.458 + 1.8 = 3.258$ m [M1W1]
(c) $s = 2.9 - 1.8 = 1.1$; $a = -10$; $u = 5.4$
$s = ut + \frac{1}{2}at^2$; $1.1 = 5.4t - 5t^2$; $5t^2 - 5.4t + 1.1 = 0$
$t = 0.27$ and 0.81 seconds [M1W2]

7. (a)

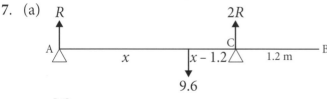

[1]
(b) $R + 2R = 9.6$
Reaction at $A = 3.2$ N; Reaction at $C = 6.4$ N [2]
(c) Moments at A: $6.4 \times (2x - 1.2) = 9.6x$, so $x = 2.4$
So length of plank $= 2.4 \times 2 = 4.8$ m [M1W2]

8. (a)

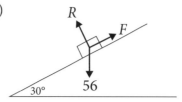

[2] ([1] for 1 correct force]
(b) $F = 56 \sin 30 = 28$ N [1]
(c) $R = 56 \cos 30 = 48.50$ N [1]
(d)

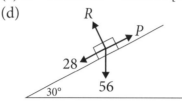

$P = 28 + 56 \sin 30 = 56$ N [M1W1]

Revision Exercise 4

1. (a) Aideen: $u = 0$; $a = 0.4$; $t = 7$
$v = u + at = 0.4 \times 7 = 2.8$ m/s

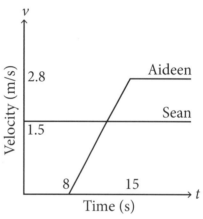

[2]
(b) Sean: Let T s = time Sean walks until Aideen
overtakes him. Distance Sean walks $= 1.5T$
Aideen: 1st part distance $= \frac{1}{2} \times 7 \times 2.8 = 9.8$
2nd part distance $= 2.8(T - 15) = 2.8T - 42$
so $9.8 + 2.8T - 42 = 1.5T$; $T = 24.77$ s [M2W2]
(c) $1.5 \times 24.77 = 37.15$ or 37.16 m [1]

2. (a) $v = u + at$; $14 = 2 + 3t$; $t = 4$s [M1W1]
(b) $s = \frac{1}{2}t(u + v) = \frac{1}{2} \times 4 \times (2 + 14) = 32$ m
[M1W1]

3. (a) $s = \frac{1}{2}t(u + v) = (15\mathbf{i} - 40\mathbf{j})$ m/s [M1W1]
(b) $v = u + at$; $(0\mathbf{i} + 0\mathbf{j}) = (4\mathbf{i} - 13\mathbf{j}) + 10a$
$a = (-0.4\mathbf{i} + 1.3\mathbf{j})$ m/s^2 [M1W1]
(c) $F = ma = 15(-0.4\mathbf{i} + 1.3\mathbf{j}) = (-6\mathbf{i} + 19.5\mathbf{j})$ N [1]
(d) $\sqrt{(-6)^2 + 19.5^2} = \sqrt{416.25} = 20.40$ N [1]

4. (a)

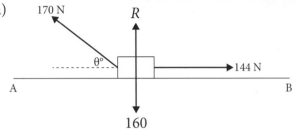

Resolve horizontally: 170 cos θ = 144;
θ = 32.11° [M1W1]
(b) Resolve vertically:
170 sin 32.11 + R = 160; R = 69.64 N [M1W1]

5. (a) $u = 0$; $v = 18$; $s = 108$
$v^2 = u^2 + 2as$; $324 = 0 + 216a$; $a = 1.5$ m/s^2 [1]
(b) $F = ma$; $3910 – 1456 = (M + 480) \times 1.5$
$M = 1156$ kg [M1W1]
(c) $0.684 \times 1156 = 790.704$ N [1]
(d) $1456 – 790.704 = 665.296$ N [1]
(e) Trailer: $F = ma$; $T – 665.296 = 480 \times 1.5$;
$T = 1385.296$ N [M1W1]
(f) Trailer: $F = ma$; $–665.296 = 480a$; $a = – 1.386$
$u = 18$; $v = 0$; $v = u + at$; $0 = 18 – 1.386t$; $t = 12.99$ s
[M1W1]

6. (a)

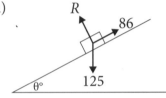

[2] ([1] for 1 or 2 correct forces)
(b) 125 sin θ = 86; θ = 43.47° [1]
(c) $R = 125$ cos 43.47 = 90.71 or 90.72 N [1]
(d) $u = 0$; $t = 7$; $s = 1.5$
$s = ut + \frac{1}{2}at^2$; $1.5 = \frac{1}{2} \times a \times 7^2$; $a = 0.0612$
$F = ma$; $Q – 125$ sin 43.47
$= 12.5 \times 0.0612$; $Q = 86.76$ or 86.77 N [M1W2]

7. (a)

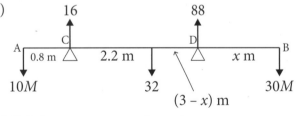

[2] ([1] for 1 or 2 correct forces)
(b) $10M + 32 + 30M = 16 + 88$; $M = 1.8$ kg at A;
$3M = 5.4$ kg at B [M1W1]
(c) Moments at B:
$88x + 16 \times 5.2 = 32 \times 3 + 18 \times 6$; $x = 1.37$m
[M1W1]

(d)

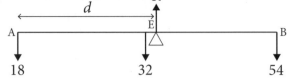

$R = 18 + 32 + 54 = 104$
Moments at A: $104d = 32 \times 3 + 54 \times 6$; $d = 4.04$ m
[M1W1]

8. (a)

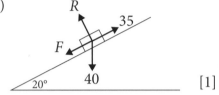

[1]

(b) $u = 3$; $v = 8$; $s = 10$
$v^2 = u^2 + 2as$; $8^2 = 3^2 + (2 \times 10a)$; $a = 2.75$
$35 – F – 40$ sin 20 $= 4 \times 2.75$; $F = 10.32$ N [M1W1]
(c) $–10.32 – 40$ sin 20 $= 4a$; $a = –6$
$u = 8$; $v = 0$; $v = u + at$; $0 = 8 – 6t$; $t = 1.33$ s
[M1W1]

Revision Exercise 5

1. (a)

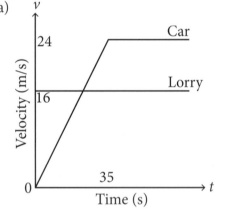

[2]

(b) Lorry: Let T sec = time when car overtakes
lorry. So distance lorry travels = $16T$
Car: Distance travelled
$= \frac{1}{2}(T + T – 35) \times 24 = 12(2T – 35) = 24T – 420$
So: $24T – 420 = 16T$; giving $T = 52.5$ s [M2W2]
(c) $16 \times 52.5 = 840$ m [1]

2. (a) $v = u + at$; so $0 = 6 + 8a$; so $a = –0.75$
Deceleration = 0.75 m/s^2 [M1W1]
(b) $s = \frac{1}{2}t(u + v) = \frac{1}{2} \times 8 \times (6 + 0) = 24$ m [M1W1]

3. (a) $x + 5 – 7 = 0$; so $x = 2$
$3 – 2y + 10 = 0$; so $y = 6.5$ [2]
(b) $F = ma$; so $–7\mathbf{i} + 10\mathbf{j} = 4a$
giving $a = (–1.75\mathbf{i} + 2.5\mathbf{j})$ m/s^2 [M1W1]
(c) tan θ = 2.5 ÷ 1.75; so θ = 55° [M1W1]